My book about me

Stick a photograph of yourself here.

The story of my life

By *Matthew camin*

Age *5*

DK

DORLING KINDERSLEY

London • New York • Stuttgart • Moscow

All About Me

I've measured the length of all these things:

My longest finger is . . . .

My big toe is . . . .

My longest strand of hair is . . . .

My nose is . . . . .

My ear is . . . .

My head is . . . . .

My waist is . . . . . .

I'm much, much taller than you!

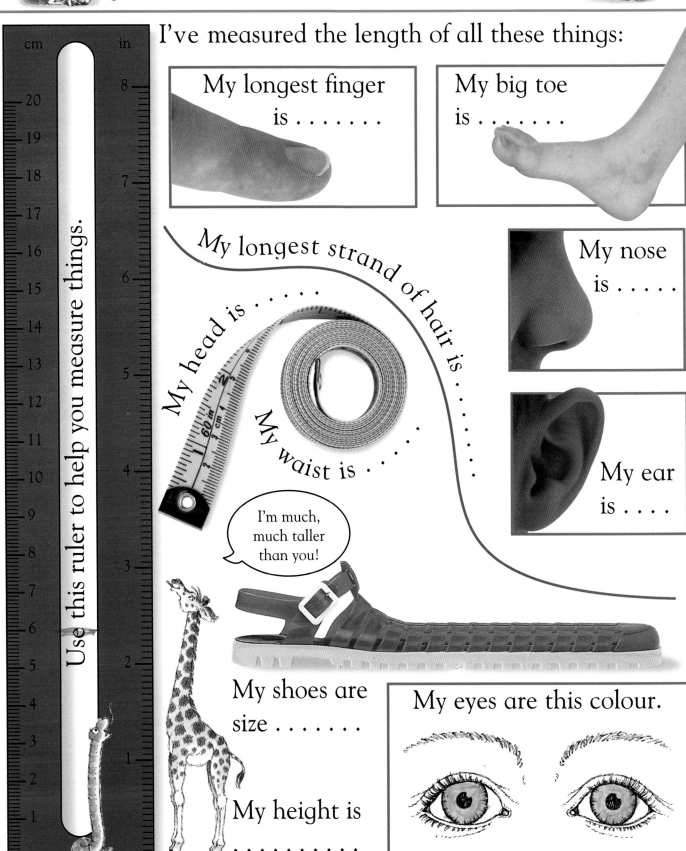

Use this ruler to help you measure things.

My shoes are size . . . .

My eyes are this colour.

My height is . . . .

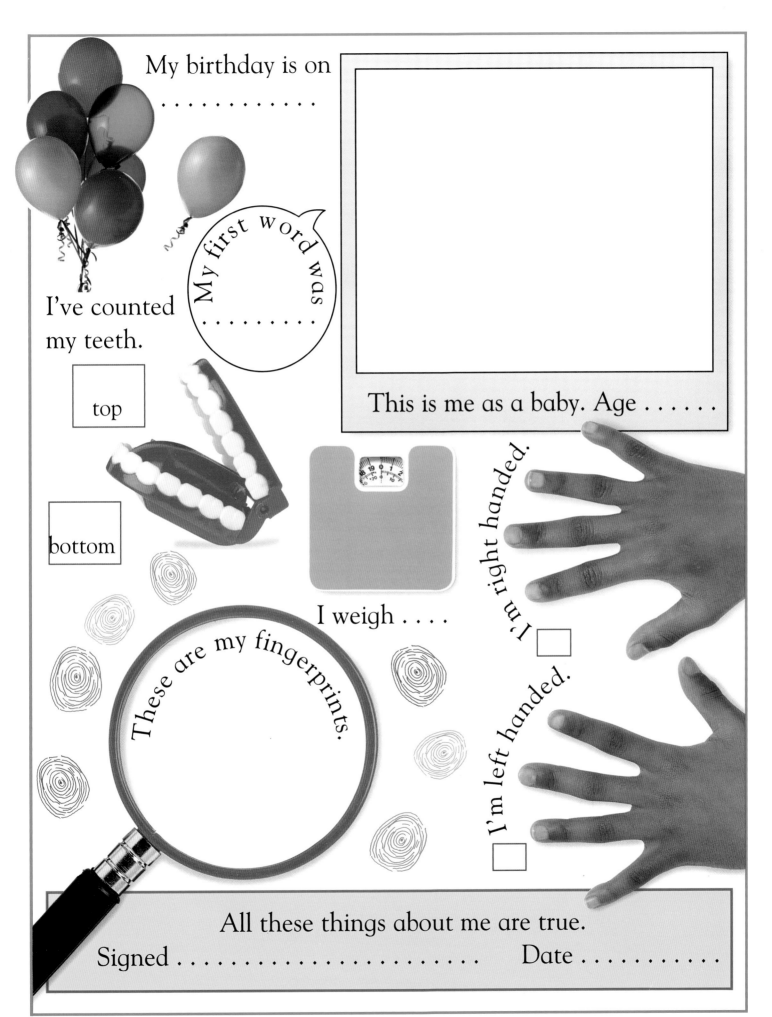

My birthday is on

. . . .

My first word was

. . . .

I've counted my teeth.

top

bottom

This is me as a baby. Age . . . .

I weigh . . . . .

I'm right handed.

I'm left handed.

These are my fingerprints.

All these things about me are true.

Signed . . . .   Date . . . .

5

My Family

This is a photo of my family.

The youngest person in my family is aged . . . .

The oldest person in my family is aged . . . .

I've collected some family autographs.

My parents

My brothers and sisters

My aunts and uncles

My cousins

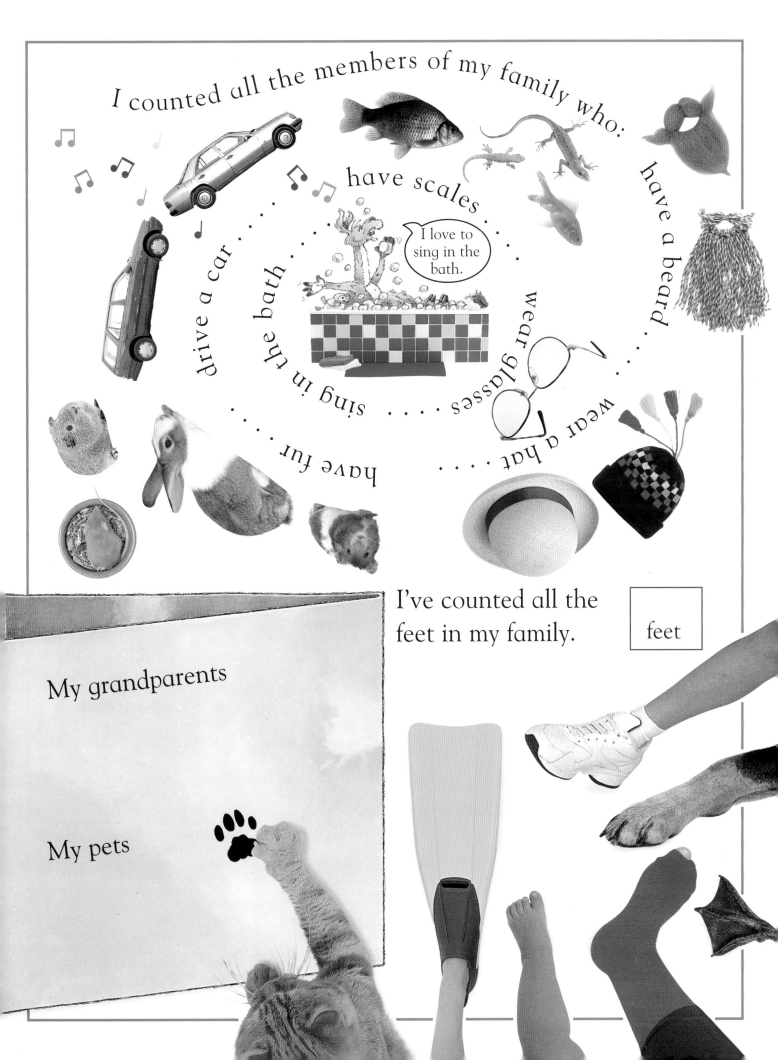

I counted all the members of my family who:

have scales . . .

have a beard . . .

wear glasses . . .

wear a hat . . .

have fur . . .

sing in the bath . . .

I love to sing in the bath.

drive a car . . .

I've counted all the feet in my family.

feet

My grandparents

My pets

My Home

People send letters to me at this address.

What a lot of post!

. . . .

. . . .

. . . .

This is where my home is:

in a town or a city ☐

in the country ☐

near the sea ☐

near a river ☐

in a desert ☐

in the mountains ☐

My telephone number is

. . . .

The country I live in is

. . . .

This is my flag.

My home looks like this.

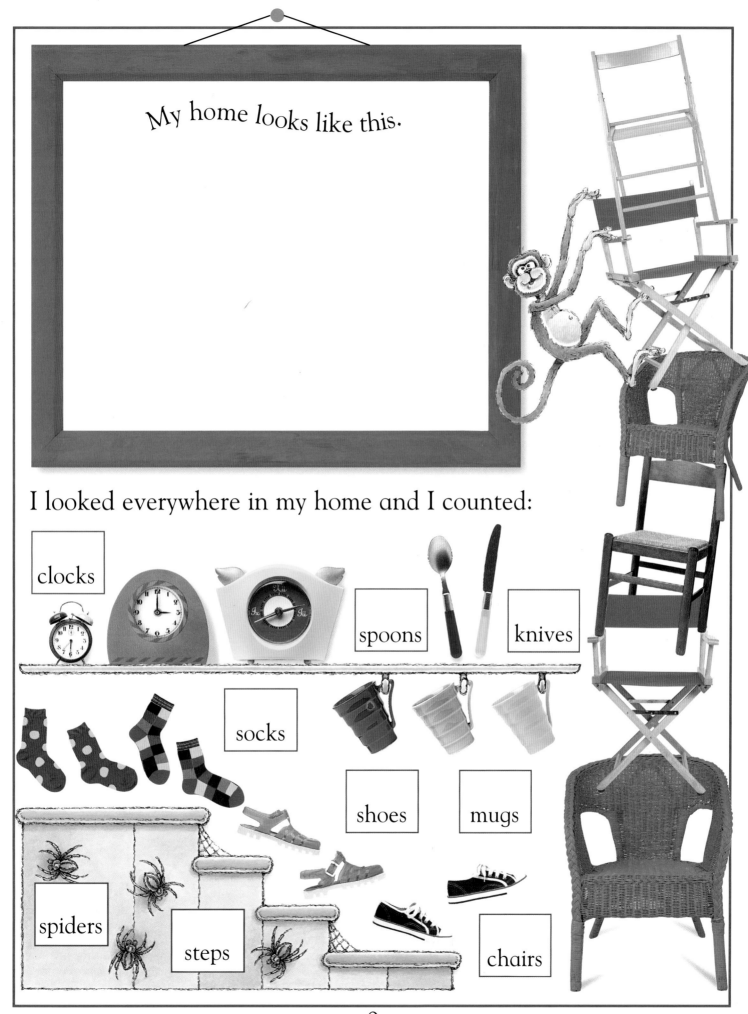

I looked everywhere in my home and I counted:

clocks

spoons

knives

socks

shoes

mugs

spiders

steps

chairs

My School

School begins at this time.

I go to school:

by car ☐

by bus ☐

by boat ☐

on foot ☐

by bike ☐

by train ☐

My school is called . . . .

. . . .

I'm in class . . . .

This is a drawing of my schoolfriends.

At school, I enjoy:

painting ☐

I love art lessons best!

writing ☐

reading ☐

8 + 2 = ☐

doing sums ☐

playing music ☐

playing games ☐

doing experiments ☐

This is a drawing of my teacher.

I've counted the children in my class.

girls ☐
boys ☐

School ends at this time.

My Friends

Best Friend Fact File

Name . . . .

Age . . . .

Phone number . . . .

Where we met . . . .

. . . .

. . . .

. . . .

This is a drawing of my best friend.

These are drawings of three of my other friends.

my funniest friend

my oldest friend

my newest friend

Name . . . .   Name . . . .   Name . . . .

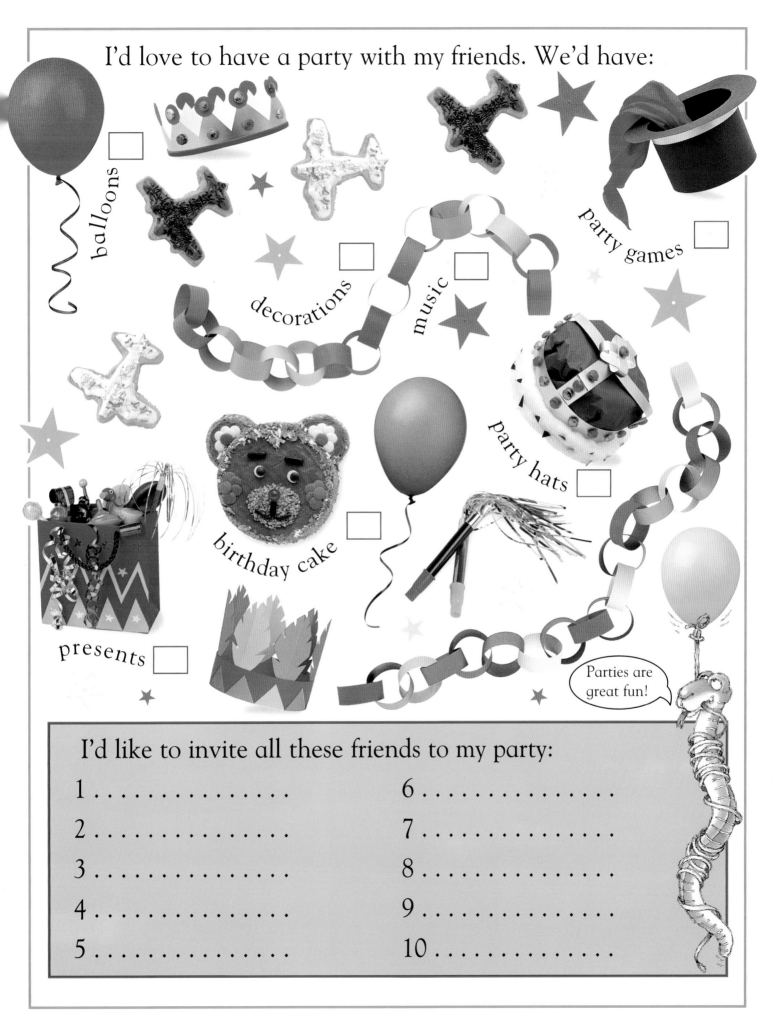

I'd love to have a party with my friends. We'd have:

balloons ☐

decorations ☐

music ☐

party games ☐

party hats ☐

birthday cake ☐

presents ☐

Parties are great fun!

I'd like to invite all these friends to my party:

1 . . . .

2 . . . .

3 . . . .

4 . . . .

5 . . . .

6 . . . .

7 . . . .

8 . . . .

9 . . . .

10 . . . .

My Fun Time

I've ticked the activities I really enjoy:

playing board-games ☐

playing the guitar ☐

playing tennis ☐

playing Frisbee® ☐

skiing ☐

dressing up ☐

fishing ☐

skateboarding ☐

dancing ☐

The activity I like doing best of all is
....
....

playing basketball ☐

swimming ☐

I like collecting
· · · · · · · ·
· · · · · · · ·

My kite collection is brilliant!

cooking ☐

playing football ☐

doing jigsaw puzzles ☐

skipping ☐

performing magic tricks ☐

taking photos ☐

The fun things I'd love to try are
· ·
· ·

gardening ☐

My Favourite Things

grapes   melon

I like fruit, especially
. . . .

I like to drink
. . . .

cherry

pineapple   lemon

orange

strawberry

apple

banana

plum

cakes ☐

I love eating:

sweets
☐

ice cream
☐

biscuits
☐

This is my favourite meal. It's . . . .

16

I love watching

. . . .

I love to sing this song

The title of my favourite book is

. . . .

. . . .

My best toy is

. . . .

. . . .

My favourite animal is

. . . .

Pick me!

toucan

fish

dolphin

horse

tortoise

frog

tiger

penguin

duck

snail

17

My Record Breakers

Here are some of my all-time best records.

This is the latest I've ever been to bed.

Here's the funniest joke I know.

. . . .

. . . .

. . . .

. . . .

I'm a record breaker, I can:

- skip with a rope ☐
- count to 100 ☐
- do 3 cartwheels ☐
- say the whole alphabet backwards ☐

This certificate proves it!

The **tallest** building I've ever been to is

. . . .

. . . .

. . . .

The **biggest** animal I've seen is . . . .

The hairiest creature I've touched is . . . .

The smelliest thing I've smelt is . . . .

The tiniest animal I've ever seen is . . . . . .

I'm whizzing along!

K 3215

The **longest** journey I've ever made is . . . .

The hottest place I've been to is . . . .

My Secrets

Here are some top-secret things about me.

This is my secret love.

I hate being tickled in these places

. . . .

. . . .

. . . .

My naughty secret is

. . . .

. . . .

My most secret wish is

. . . .

. . . .

I've saved up this much money.

. . . .

Some things frighten me!
I'm a little scared of:

snakes ☐

dinosaurs ☐

the dark ☐

ghosts ☐

big spiders ☐

small spiders ☐

bats ☐

beetles ☐

But the thing that frightens me most is

. . . .
. . . .

lizards ☐

Here's my secret mirror message.

. . . .
. . . .

I looked in a mirror to write this secret message. Now you try!

ZYXWVUTƧЯQPOИM⅃KႱIHGﬄƎⱭϽꓭA

My Future

When I grow up, I want to be:

a pilot and fly around the world ☐

an accountant ☐ ☐

an astronaut and fly a rocket to Mars ☐

a doctor and help people ☐

a brave firefighter ☐

a farmer ☐

a famous musician ☐

a vet ☐

an amazing juggler ☐

This is tricky!

a brilliant scientist ☐

an athlete and win trophies ☐

I'd also
really like to be
. . . .